The SKY

by Ariane Dewey

GREEN TIGER PRESS
Published by Simon & Schuster
New York • London • Toronto • Sydney • Tokyo • Singapore

GREEN TIGER PRESS
Simon & Schuster Building
Rockefeller Center
1230 Avenue of the Americas
New York, New York 10020
Copyright © 1993 by Ariane Dewey
All rights reserved including
the right of reproduction
in whole or in part in any form.
GREEN TIGER PRESS is an imprint
of Simon & Schuster.
Designed by Sylvia Frezzolini
and Ariane Dewey.
Manufactured in the
United States of America.

10 9 8 7 6 5 4 3 2 1

Library of Congress
Cataloging-in-Publication Data
Dewey, Ariane.
  The sky / by Ariane Dewey.
  p.   cm.
Summary: A look at the sky, both
fancifully and realistically,
both pictorially and verbally,
and always poetically.
  [1. Sky—Fiction.] I. Title.
PZ7.D5228Sk 1993   92-25222
[E]—dc20   CIP
ISBN: 0-671-77835-8   AC

The Sky is not the limit.

Look at the sky.

It's empty.

No it isn't.

The sun is up there shining.

Watch the wind breezily gather wisps of mist into clouds.

They puff and billow, big and broad, filling the sky.

Soon rain sprinkles, falls, then pours down.

It's raining, it's pouring,
the old man is snoring.

When the wind is in the east,
It's neither good for man nor beast.
When the wind is in the west,
Then the weather's always best.

When the clouds appear like rocks and towers,
Then the earth's refreshed with frequent showers.

Rain on the green grass, and rain on the tree,
And rain on the house top, but not on me.
When the dew is on the grass, Rain will never come to pass.

Rain at night, sailors delight.

Rainbow at noon, rain very soon.

Rainbow at night, sailors delight.

When the fog goes up the mountain hopping,
Then the rain comes down the mountain dropping.

When a cow tries to scratch its ear,
It means a shower is very near.
When it thumps its ribs with its tail,
Look out for thunder, lightning, hail.

Hark, I hear the asses bray,
We shall have some rain today.

Rain rain go away and come again another day.

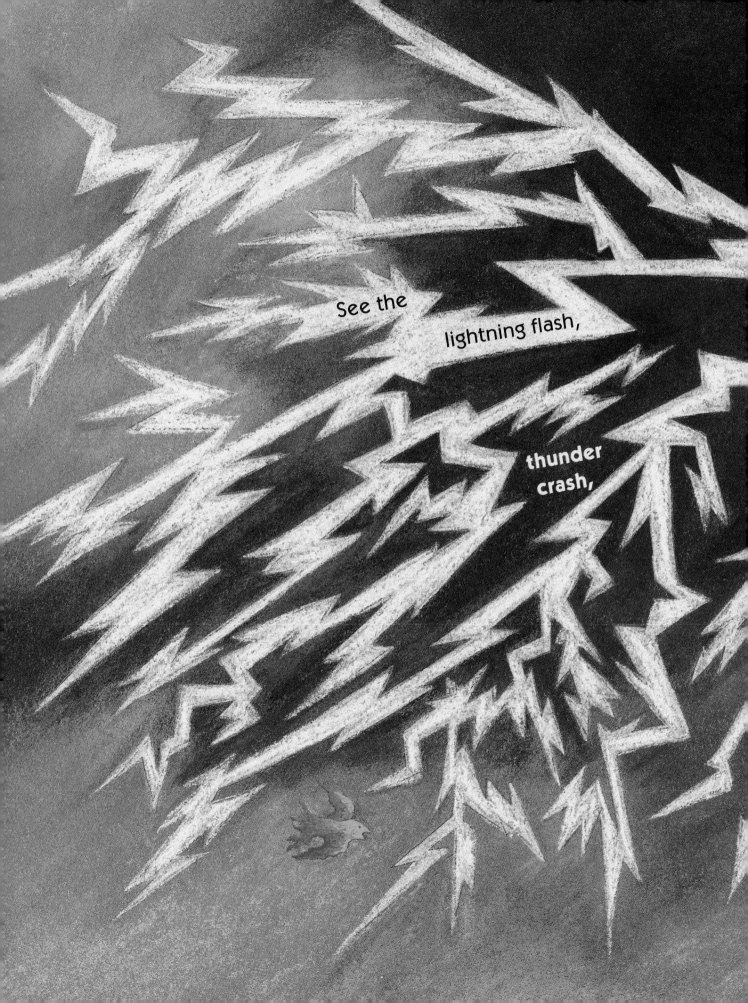

and sleet slash down.

Look out for the

HAILSTONES!

Hooray,

the storm

has blown away

leaving two

rainbows.

Now the sky
is buzzing

with birds,

bugs, and
butterflies.

Airplanes, kites, gliders,

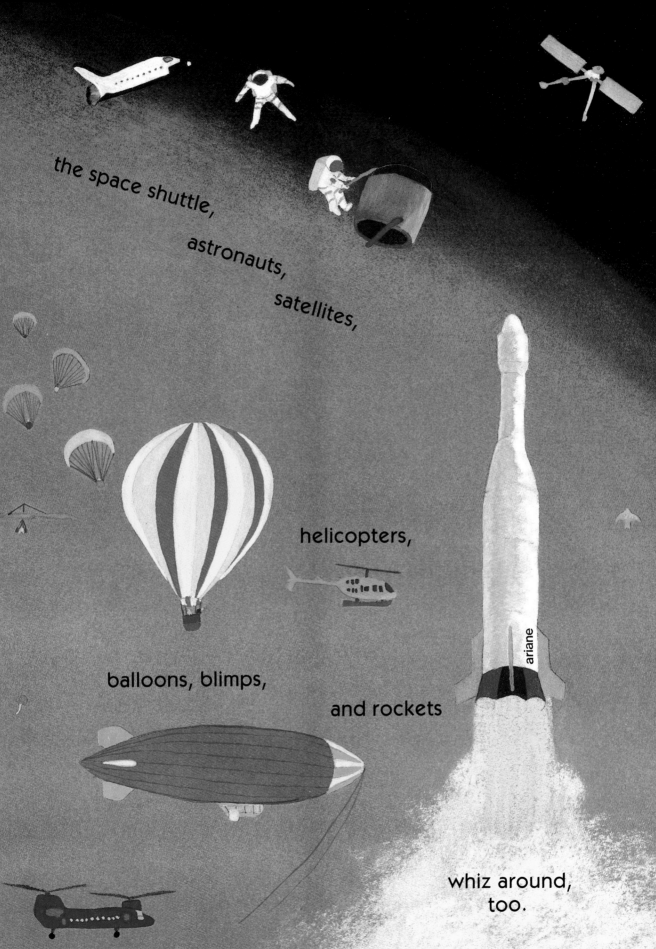

the space shuttle,

astronauts,

satellites,

helicopters,

balloons, blimps,

and rockets

ariane

whiz around,
too.

Imagine what else might be up there.

flying saucers,

UFOs,

dragons,

griffins,

superheroes

cherubim,

vampires

Tengu,

witches,

ghosts,

Leo, Pegasus, angels, cupids, the Firebird, Santa Claus, and fairies.

Sad to say, sometimes the sky looks dreadful.

Soot, smog and smoke, often clog the air with dirt.

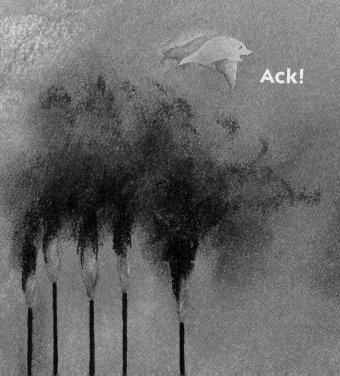

Ack!

The sky can be really frightful when the wind whips itself into a howling hurricane,

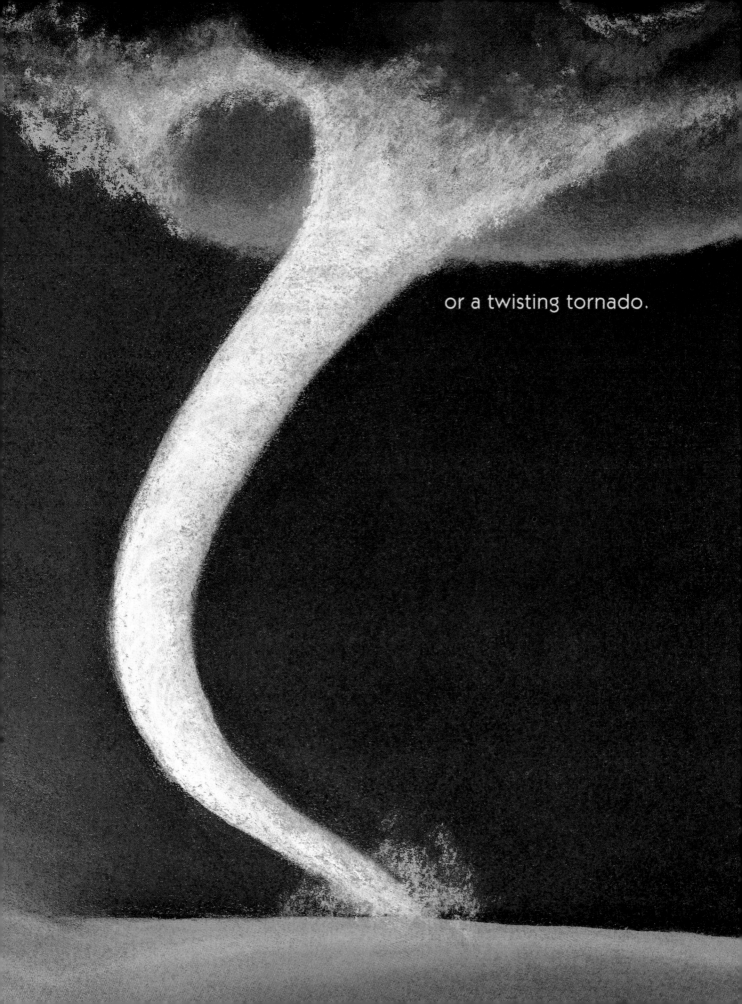

or a twisting tornado.

But usually the sky is beautiful.
Especially when snowflakes fall all day,

all night,

till land

and sky

are clean

and white.

At night the sky is spattered with starlight.

Moonshine is everywhere.

Fireflies
flicker.

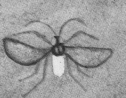

Quick, make a wish on that shooting star.

Fireworks
flash.

The aurora sighs and shimmers.

And see how the red planet throbs

as a brilliant comet passes.

Then just for a moment before dawn,
the sky looks empty again.

But is it?

No! Here comes the sun!